gage Cornerstones

Anthology 2a

Carolyn Farr   Jane Hutchison

Carol McGrail   Carol Pawlowski

Featured Illustrator: Michael Martchenko

gage EDUCATIONAL PUBLISHING COMPANY
A DIVISION OF CANADA PUBLISHING CORPORATION
Vancouver · Calgary · Toronto · London · Halifax

Copyright © 2000 Gage Educational Publishing Company
A Division of Canada Publishing Corporation

Bias Consultant: Margaret Hoogeveen

Cover Illustration: Jan Thornhill

Acknowledgments

Every reasonable effort has been made to trace ownership of copyrighted material. Information that would enable the publisher to correct any reference or credit in future editions would be appreciated.

We acknowledge the financial support of the Government of Canada through the Book Publishing Industry Development Program for our publishing activities.

24 "Fisherman Fred" by Tony D. Triggs. Illustrations by Toni Goffe. © Michael Twinn. By permission of Child's Play International. **34** "Lizzie's Invitation" Text and illustrations by Holly Keller. © 1987 Holly Keller. By permission of Greenwillow Books, a division of William Morrow and Company, Inc. **54** "Minerva Louise at School" from *Minerva Louise at School* by Janet Morgan Stoeke. © 1996 by Janet Morgan Stoeke. By permission of Dutton Children's Books, a division of Penguin Putnam Inc. **80** "Lucy's Picture" by Nicola Moon. Illustrations by Alex Ayliffe. Text © 1994 Nicola Moon. Illustrations © 1994 Alex Ayliffe. First published in the UK by Orchard Books, a division of The Watts Publishing Group Limited, 96 Leonard Street, London, EC2A 4XD. **96** "Treasure Box" from *The Kids Can Press Jumbo Book of Crafts* by Judy Ann Sadler and illustrated by Caroline Price. By permission of Kids Can Press Ltd. Toronto. Text ©1997 by Judy Ann Sadler. **104** "Busy Beaver" from *Beavers* by Deborah Hodge. By permission of Kids Can Press Ltd., Toronto. Illustrations by Pat Stephens. Text © 1998 by Deborah Hodge. Illustrations © 1998 by Pat Stephens. **122** "Raven Bringing Light to the World" reviewed and edited by Robert Davidson. **126** "There are No Polar Bears Here!" by Catherine A. Simpson. Illustrations by Joanne Snook. Text © 1995 by Catherine A. Simpson. Illustrations © 1995 by Joanne Snook. By permission of Creative Publishing International.

Canadian Cataloguing in Publication Data

Main entry under title:

Gage cornerstones : Canadian language arts. Anthology, 2a

ISBN 0-7715-1242-2

1. Readers (Primary). I. Farr, Carolyn, et al.
II. Martchenko, Michael.
III. Title: Cornerstones: Canadian language arts.
IV. Anthology, 2a.

PE1119.G234 1999   428.6   C99-931885-3

Photo Credits

74 R. Konig/Jacana/Publiphoto, **75 top, bottom** Murray Johnson, **76 top** Marco, **bottom** Murray Johnson, **77** Teyss/Publiphoto, **96-99, 121, 122 middle** Dave Starrett, **103 bottom, 104 top, 116** Photo of Dozay Christmas by permission of Arlene Dozay Christmas c/o University College of Cape Breton Press. **116-140** Images of Canadian coins by permission of Royal Canadian Mint. Image on $200 coin *Raven Bringing Light to the World* by permission of Robert Davidson. **117 top** Patricia Armstrong, **117** © Robert Bateman. Reproduction rights courtesy Boshkung, Inc. **118** Image of loon taken from *A Northern Alphabet* ©1982 by Ted Harrison, published by Tundra Books. **119** Emily Carr. *Untitled* (1929-1939), VAG 42.3.123. By permission of Vancouver Art Gallery/Trevor Mills. Photo of Emily Carr. Image 27 429 (Emily Carr in England 1901-02). By permission of B.C. Archives and PAN Productions. **120 top** Ted Levin, Animals/Animals, **120 bottom** Bertram G. Murray Jr., Animals/Animals, **142 far left** Visuals Unlimited, **top left** Bildagentur Schuster/Layda, **middle left** Gerard Lacz/Publiphoto, **bottom** Publiphoto, **143 middle left** Tom J. Ulrich/Visuals Unlimited, **top** Gerard Lacz/Publiphoto, **top right** Gerard Lacz/Publiphoto, **bottom right** Bildagentur Schuster/Degenhardt.

Illustrations

6-13, 44-51, 64-73, 90-95 Michael Martchenko, **14-15** Philippe Béha, **16-23** Joe Weissmann, **42-43** Sue Todd, **52-53, 102, 103 top** Anne Stanley, **78-79** Daphne McCormack, **100-101** Bryan Stewart, **108-115** Barbara Spurll, **121** Jun Park, **122** Illustrations from *Raven: A Trickster Tale from the Pacific Northwest.* © 1993 by Gerald McDermott. By permission of Harcourt, Inc., **140-141** Scot Ritchie, **144 top, bottom** Bill Suddick

ISBN 0-7715-1242-2
2 3 4 5 6 BP 03 02 01 00
Printed and bound in Canada.

Cornerstones Development Team

HERE ARE THE PEOPLE WHO WORKED HARD TO MAKE
THIS BOOK EXCITING FOR YOU!

WRITING TEAM
Carolyn Farr
Jane Hutchison
Carol McGrail
Carol Pawlowski

EDITORIAL TEAM
Gage Editorial
Joe Banel
Elizabeth Long
Darleen Rotozinski

FIRST FOLIO TEAM
Fran Cohen
Francine Geraci
Jane McWhinney
Alison Reid

GAGE PRODUCTION
Anna Kress
Bev Crann

**DESIGN, ART DIRECTION
& ELECTRONIC ASSEMBLY**
Pronk&Associates/David Montle

ADVISORY TEAM
Jane Abernethy, Chipman & Fredericton SD, NB
Gwen Bartnik, Vancouver SB, BC
Susan Boehnke, Durham DSB, ON
Lisa Bond, Catholic Independent Schools of
     Vancouver Archdiocese, BC
Marg Craig, Lambton-Kent DSB, ON
Sheila Devine Ross, Southwest Regional SB, NS
Laurel Galt, Durham DSB, ON
Gloria Gustafson, Coquitlam DSB, BC
Lise Hawkins, Toronto DSB, ON
Sharon Kinakin, Langley SD #35, BC
Jane Koberstein, Mission DSB, BC
Irene Kovats, Calgary CSSB, AB
Rosemary Lloyd, Durham DSB, ON
Martin MacDonald, Strait Regional SB, NS
Sharon Morris, Toronto CDSB, ON
Cheryl Norman, Delta SD #37, BC
Jennifer Pinches, Calgary CSD, AB
Joanne Pizzuto, Windsor DSB, ON
Pearl Reimer, Edmonton PSB, AB
Maureen Rodniski, Winnipeg SD, MB
Patricia Rooney, Wellington County CDSB, ON
Barbara Rushton, Annapolis Valley Regional SB, NS
Lynn Strangway, Simcoe DSB, ON
Anna Totten, Toronto CDSB, ON
Doreen M. Valverde, Southwest Regional SB, NS
Suzanne Witkin, Toronto DSB, ON

Contents

🍁 Canadian Content

Getting to Know You

Back at School

Hooray! We're back at school again.
Holidays are done.
Look who's on the playground.
Hi there, everyone!

Hi there, Ted and Bud and Kim,
Anna and Dan and Gus.
Hi there, Robin in the tree.
Get down here with us!

There's Miss Day and Mr. Gold.
There's the principal, too.
Over there is Mr. Parks,
Our teacher, who is new!

There are children on the sidewalk,
There are children by the wall,
There are children on the green grass.
We're back here — one and all!

The Secret Code

"Look at the letter my friend Raj sent me!" said Kim.

"What does it say?" asked Ted.

"Show Mr. Parks. He'll know," said Bud.

"Mr. Parks," said Kim. "Look what Raj sent me."
Mr. Parks looked at the letter. He said, "This is
marvellous. We can have lots of fun finding out
what it says."

Raj's Secret Code

What did Raj tell Kim? Use this code to read Raj's letter.

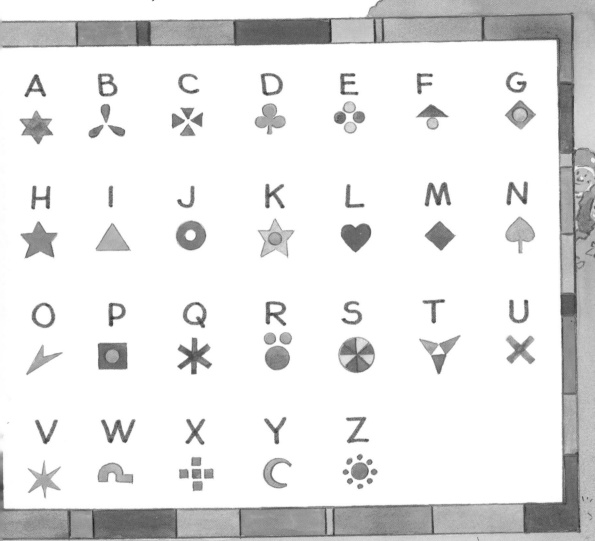

Your Name is a Super Thing

Our Classroom Rules

* Be kind to each other.
* Respect each other.
* Take care of our classroom.

Tidy Tip

Working as a tidy team, we can make classroom gle Tidy tidy as you go, then those me never grow.

13

A Beautiful Thing

In sand
washed by waves
with a stick

in air
gently teased
with my finger

on slippery
smooth glass
wet with rain

on paper
in a rainbow
of colours

I write my name

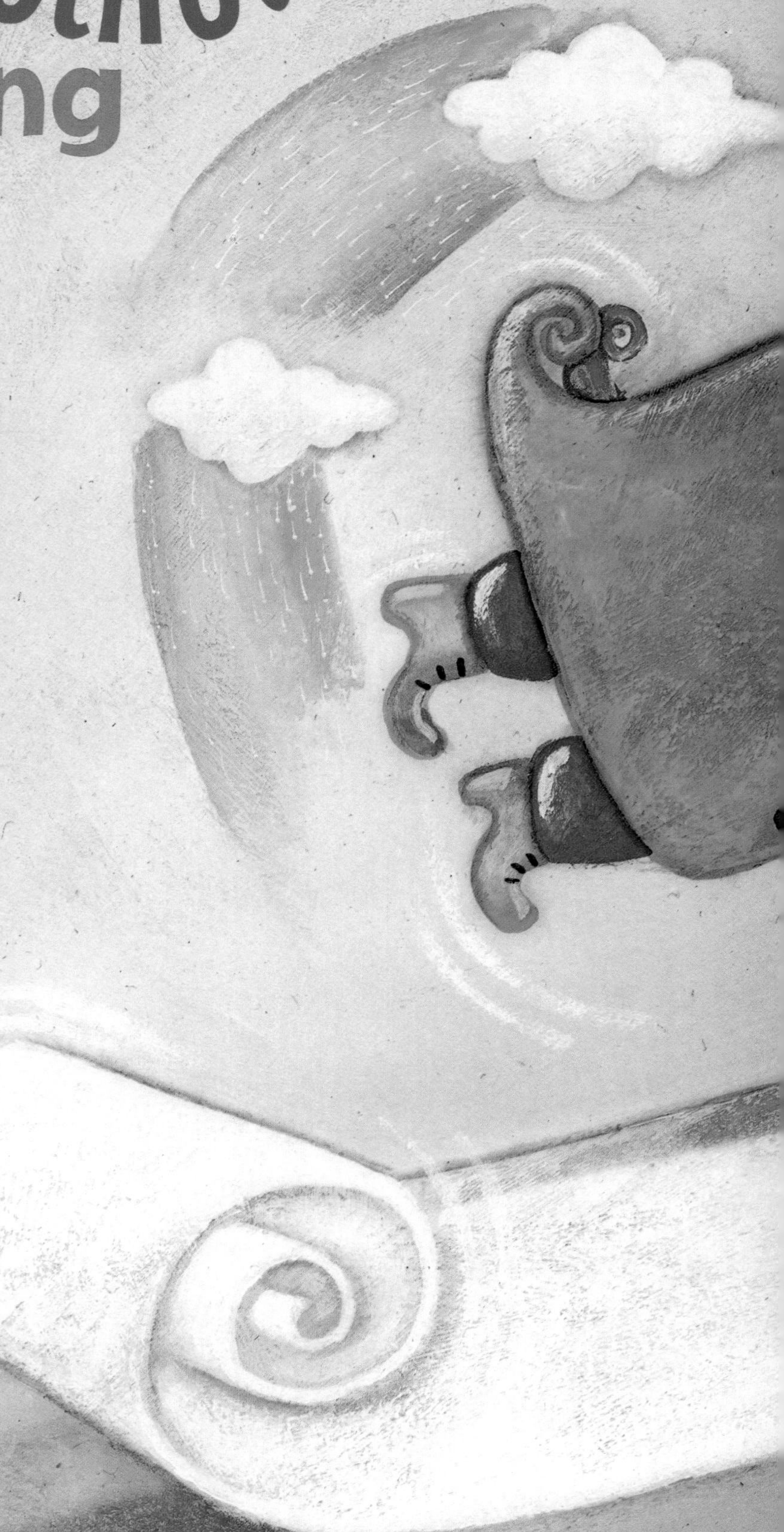

A Special Name

Pictures by Joe Weissmann

Once upon a time, in a faraway land, a baby boy was born. His mother and father loved him very much. "We must find a name that is just right for him," said his father. "Then we will have a big party."

But no matter how hard his mother and father
tried, they could not find the right name. By the time
he was two years old, he still did not have a name.

"Our son is not a baby any more. He never stops. He runs around all day so his clothes are always rumpled. He wiggles all night so his sheets are always rumpled. Let's call him Rumple," grumbled his father.

"Well, I do not like the name Rumple," said his mother. "He just needs more time. I'm sure we will find a special name for him."

By the time the little boy was four, he was into everything. He played his father's trumpet at midnight. He drummed 'Rum-Tum-Tum' all day on his little drum. He liked to jump on his mother's spinning wheel and spin around. He just never stopped!

"I think a special name for him is Sit Still," grumbled his father. "Maybe then he will stop."

"Oh, no," said his mother. "I do not like the name, Sit Still. I'm sure that we will find a special name for him. He just needs more time."

By the time the boy was six, he could do amazing things. He could make yarn on his mother's spinning wheel. He could spell very well. Best of all, he could make up riddles that fooled his sister every time. She could never guess his riddles!

One day, the boy went into his father's workshop to make something out of wood. Before long, he came stomping out on two tall stilts.

"What an amazing boy you are," laughed his father. "You have made stilts! Now I know your special name." Father winked at Mother. "Now we can have our party."

The special day came. Everyone sang and danced and had a wonderful time. When they saw the cake, they cheered. It had a special name on it – **Rumplestiltskin**. The little boy ran around all day and night singing "Rumplestiltskin is my name and one day it will bring me fame."

Now why do you think his mother and father gave him that name?

Fisherman Fred

Story by Tony Triggs   Pictures by Toni Goffe

Fisherman Fred went fishing each night...

And, every day, he rode around the town on his rusty old bike, calling, "Fish for sale! Fish for sale!" He had almost no time left for anything else.

One day, Fred was selling fish to his friend Bill, when he had an idea.

"I'll give up my bike and sell fish from my front room! You are a genius with paint, Bill. Why don't you paint a sign to go over my front door?"

Bill came at once. Soon the sign was gleaming across the front of Fred's house.

FRESH FISH SOLD HERE

But very few customers came to buy fish.

Later that day, a man pointed at the sign and laughed. "You don't need to say the fish is fresh. You couldn't sell it, otherwise!"

"Perhaps he's right," thought Fisherman Fred when the man had gone. "I'd better hide the word **fresh**."

FISH SOLD HERE

Fred climbed his ladder and nailed a board over part of the sign. Now, there were only three words, not four. But very few customers came to buy fish.

A girl came along with her dog. "Why does your sign say **here**? The sign is here, so the fish must be here, too, mustn't it?"

So, Fred decided to hide the word **here**.

Now, there were only two words on the sign. But very few customers came to buy fish.

Next, a woman stared at the sign. "Surely, you don't need to say **sold**," she giggled. "We know you don't give your fish away!"

Fred agreed. He nailed on another board. Only a single word was left. But very few customers came to buy fish.

Then, Charlie Bloggs, the police officer, said, "You don't need a sign, at all. Why say **fish**, when you've sold fish for years?"

Fred covered the last word. Then, he fetched some brown paint and made the boards look like new. But very few customers came to the house.

Just as he finished, an old man came up. He wanted to buy a can of paint. "I can tell by the smell that you sell paint," he said. "But wouldn't it be better to have a proper sign?"

"Aha!" sighed Fred. "So, I do need a sign, after all!" He climbed his ladder and took off one of the painted boards. But very few customers came to the house.

A boy whizzed by on his skateboard. "Hello, Mr. Fish!" he called rudely.

So, Fred took off another board.

Now, there were two words on the sign again. But very few customers came to the house.

"They still think I sell my fish in the street," thought Fred. "But I sell it here and the sign should say so."

Fred took off another board.

Now, there were three words again. But very few customers came to the house. Then, along came Bill. "You've spoiled my sign," he said angrily. "That big space in front of **fish** looks all wrong."

So, Fred took off the last board. Now, there were four words on the sign again. But, still, very few customers came to Fred's house.

In the meantime, the fish wasn't so fresh.

Fred called the cats' home.... The lady was one of his best customers.

"I'm afraid this fish is not fresh," explained Fred, "but it is FREE."

"Thank you," she said. "I'll come over right away. I wondered what had happened to you."

Fred told her about the sign Bill had made. "I noticed it at once," she smiled. "It is a lovely sign. But there is one thing wrong with it....

"Now, you go fishing and I will talk to Bill."

It was still dark, when Fred arrived home.

The next morning, when he drew back the curtains, all his old customers were waiting outside.

Fred rubbed his eyes. He hurried to wash and get dressed. When he opened the door, everyone cheered.

The lady from the cats' home was there. The cats had come, too, to say thank you to Fred.

"You forgot to put your name on the sign," she said. "**Fred** stands for honesty and cheerfulness and fresh fish."

"Nothing is more important than your good name!"

Lizzie's Invitation

Story and pictures by Holly Keller

Alex got one and Loren got one.
Tommy got one, too. Lizzie
knew because she could see it sticking out
of his back pocket.

The envelopes were blue with
yellow balloons on the front.

They were invitations to a
birthday party. Kate gave them out at
lunch time, and Lizzie didn't get one.

Lizzie took some carrot sticks out of her lunch box and went over to Kate.

"Want some carrots, Kate?" she asked. Lizzie hoped Kate still had an envelope for her.

"Sure," Kate said. "Want some raisins?"

"OK," Lizzie said. Then Kate walked away and sat with Tommy.

Lizzie took her lunch box behind the easel and ate by herself.

She painted a picture of angry faces.

"No happy faces today?" Ms. Healy asked. Lizzie just shrugged.

The next day Lizzie didn't want to go to school. "Don't you feel well?" Mama asked. Lizzie shook her head, and Mama put her into bed for a rest.

Lizzie made a birthday card for Kate, but she threw it away. She had a party for her dolls, but it wasn't any fun. So she went to sleep.

Saturday was the day of Kate's party. It was raining and Lizzie felt sad.

After breakfast she put on her raincoat and went outside.

"Don't stay out too long," Mama said.

Lizzie walked down the street to the playground. The swings were all wet, and the sandbox was muddy.

She squatted down and watched a leaf float in a puddle. She could see her face in the water.

Then there was another face.

"Hi," the other face said.

Lizzie stood up to see who was there. It was Amanda, a girl in her class.

"Want to try the see-saw?" Amanda asked. Lizzie didn't really feel like it, but she said OK.

The see-saw made a creaky sound.

Then Amanda bumped Lizzie, and Lizzie bumped Amanda. Lizzie laughed. They made big splashes in the puddles with their feet.

Amanda giggled. "My socks are all wet."

"Mine too," Lizzie said.

"Can you come over to my house?" Amanda asked.

"Aren't you going to Kate's party?" Lizzie asked.

"No," Amanda said, "I wasn't invited."

"Me either," Lizzie said. And they didn't talk about it anymore.

Amanda's mother gave Lizzie a pair of slippers to wear while her socks were drying. They were very big.

Then she called Lizzie's mother to say that Lizzie was staying to play.

There was vegetable soup for lunch. Amanda liked to put crackers in her soup, too.

After lunch, they played with Amanda's dress-up clothes.

Lizzie helped Amanda make curtains for her doll house, and they made pictures with their fingers on the foggy windows.

Amanda showed Lizzie how to make jelly cookies.

"The grape ones are the best," Amanda said, and she put some in a bag for Lizzie to take home.

When it was time for Lizzie to leave, Amanda
walked outside with her to say goodbye.

"I had a good time," Lizzie said.

"Me too," Amanda said.

"See you Monday at
school," Amanda called
when Lizzie got to the end
of the path. Lizzie waved
and took a cookie out of
the bag to eat on the
way home.

Getting There

QUEEN ST.

MAIN ST.

KING RD.

N

Maps

Maps are really amazing things.
They tell you where to go.
They lead you across the country,
From Vancouver to Chebucto.

They tell you what the land is like,
Whether it's high or low.
They tell you where it's very dry,
And where the waters flow.

Maps tell about the cities.
The streets and roads they show.
They guide you home on a wintry night,
So you won't get lost in the snow.

Maps are truly amazing things.
But the very best ones show
Where pirates hid their silver and gold
In treasure chests long ago.

SCALE

0   100   200   300   KM

Gus Gets to School

The bell rang.

Gus was late for school — AGAIN!

"Gus is always late," said Dan.

"Maybe he has a long way to go," said Ted.

Mr. Parks said, "It's time to read. Enjoy your books."

Dan and Ted began to read their books. Then Gus slid into his seat and got his book out — fast!

" Good morning, Gus," said Mr. Parks.

"Good morning, Mr. Parks," said Gus.

Mr. Parks said, "Gus, I'd like to talk to you."

Gus went over to Mr. Parks' desk. Mr. Parks showed him a paper.

"Gus, you have been late for school almost every day. Why do you think you are late so much?"

"I have a long, long, way to go," said Gus. "Maybe that's why."

Mr. Parks looked at the class address list. "Maybe I can help. When you come to school, which way do you go?"

Gus told Mr. Parks about the way he came to school.

"Hmmm," said Mr. Parks.

Mr. Parks took out a map and put an X on it.
"Look at the pictures on this map, Gus," he said.
"They help us read the map. Each picture stands for
something special. See this red rectangle? I put an X
on it. It's our school."

Mr. Parks pointed his finger along the map and showed Gus the way he had come to school. "The way you go is too long, Gus," said Mr. Parks. "Can you find a shorter way on this map?"

Gus looked at the map. "I'll try. This map is just like a maze. I like to do mazes. They're fun." Gus took his finger and made a new line on the map. "Look, Mr. Parks. I'm fast at mazes and I am fast at maps, too! I'll try my new way tomorrow."

The next morning Gus got to school ten
minutes early!

"Good morning, Mr. Parks," called Gus.

"Good morning, Gus. You are early,"
laughed Mr. Parks.

"Yes, and I have time to play, too!" said Gus.

Gus' Old Route

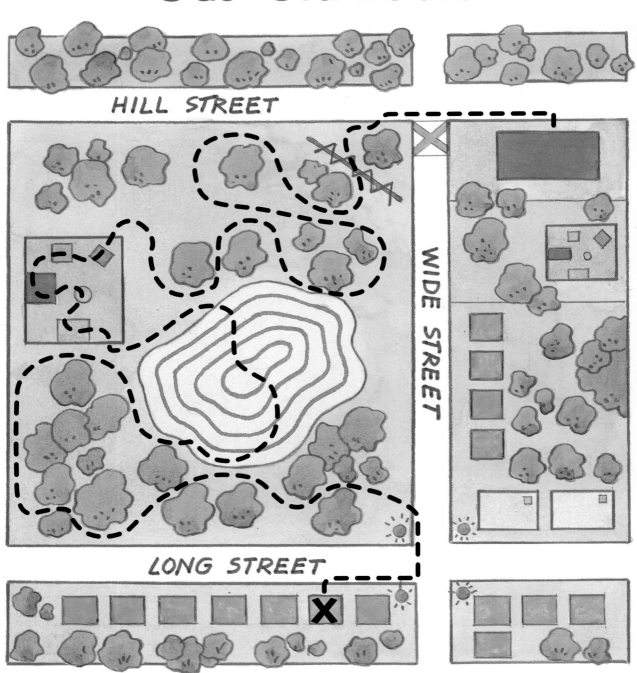

Gus' New Route

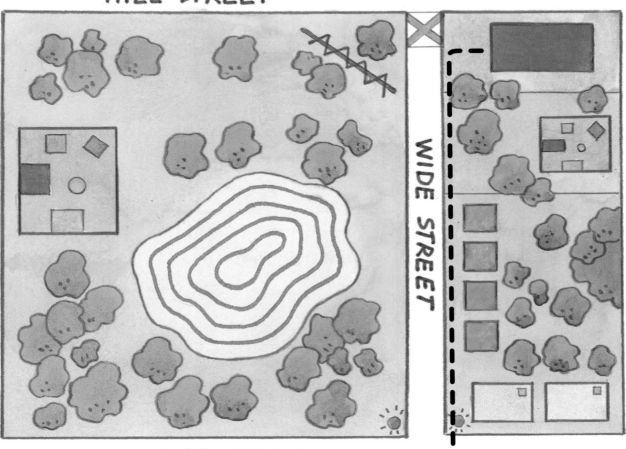

HILL STREET

WIDE STREET

LONG STREET

LEGEND

House — Street — Playground — School — Crosswalk

Tree — Hill — Fence — Apartment Building — Traffic Lights

All Kinds of Maps

Community map — A community map helps you to know where to go in a neighbourhood.

CANADA

Map of Canada — You can use this map to find places in Canada. Find where you live.

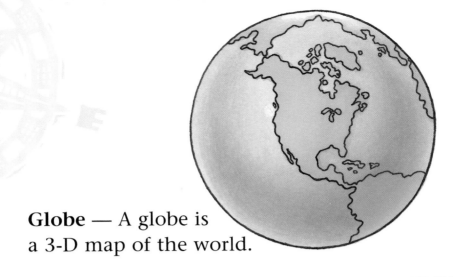

Globe — A globe is a 3-D map of the world.

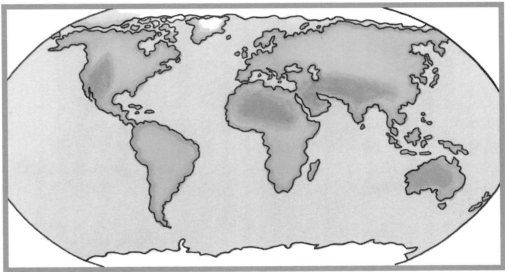

World map — A world map is the globe flattened out.

Moon map — A moon map shows you what the surface of the moon is like.

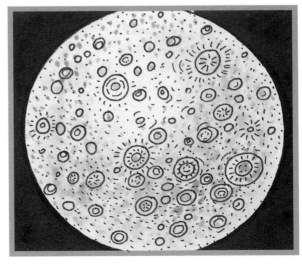

Minerva Louise
at School

Story and pictures by Janet Morgan Stoeke

One morning, Minerva Louise woke up before
everyone else.

It was a beautiful morning, so she decided to go for a walk through the tall grass.

She walked on and on.

Oh look! A big, fancy barn, thought Minerva Louise.

She watched the farmer hang his laundry out to dry...

...and she noticed that he had left the door open.

So many stalls! There must be all kinds of animals here.

Here are milking stools for the cows...

...and a pen for the pigs.

Oh, a bucket, too. It must be for feeding the chickens.

Nesting boxes! How wonderful!

Look at them all. And each one is decorated differently.

This one is all done up with ribbons.

And this one is lined with fur.

Oh my goodness, there's an EGG in this one!

But where is his mother? He'll get cold.

Well, this hay will keep you warm.

I'm sure the animals are around here somewhere.
But I have to go home now.

Minerva Louise hurried home through the tall grass.

She had some work to do.
But she knew she'd go back to the fancy barn some day...

...because it was such a wonderful place to get new ideas.

A Cranberry Adventure

PART 1
An E-mail Recipe

Cranberry Sauce
3 cups of cranberries
1 cup of sugar
1 cup of water
- Wash the cranberries.
- In a pan, mix the sugar and water.
- Bring to a boil.
- Boil for 5 minutes.
- Add the cranberries.
- Boil gently about 5 minutes.
- Remove from the heat.
- When cool, put in the refrigerator.
(Oranges and nuts can be added for extra flavour.)

"Look, Mr. Parks," said Dan. "My cousin Marie sent me an e-mail. She says she went to a cranberry marsh near Vancouver. She sent a recipe, too."

Cranberry Sauce

3 cups of cranberries

1 cup of sugar

1 cup of water

- Wash the cranberries.
- In a pan, mix the sugar and water.
- Bring to a boil.
- Boil for 5 minutes.
- Add the cranberries.
- Boil gently about 5 minutes.
- Remove from the heat.
- When cool, put in the refrigerator.

(Oranges and pears can be added for extra flavour.)

"Yummm," said Bud. "I would put that on top of ice cream."

Anna said, "I would put that on my toast."

Ted laughed, "I would make cranberry sandwiches."

Mr. Parks smiled. "Would you like to try this recipe?" he asked. "Yes!" said the children.

The class all sang as the bus rolled along.
"I love to sing all these songs," said Dan.
"I love all the beautiful coloured trees," said Gus.
"I love when we get to eat," laughed Robin.
"Look!" called Ted, "We are at the cranberry marsh!"

As the children got off the bus, Anna asked, "Where are all the cranberry trees?"

Mr. Parks laughed. "You will see," he said.

Just then a big wagon, pulled by a tractor, stopped by their bus.

"All aboard the Berry Bus!" called the driver.

The children climbed aboard. Everyone laughed as the wagon wobbled along the dirt pathway beside the water.

"This road is not very wide," said Robin. "I hope we don't fall into the pond!"

Mr. Parks laughed. "This is not a pond, Robin. This is called a marsh or a bog. Each year this part of the marsh is filled with water so that something special can happen."

"Where are the cranberry trees?" whispered Anna to Gus. "All I see are weeds in the water."

Just then the driver called out, "Look to your right and you will see the cranberries in the marsh."

Everyone looked but they didn't see any trees with cranberries. All they saw were beautiful red berries glistening under the water.

"Look! There are treasures in the marsh," said Mr. Parks.

"Treasure!" yelled Robin. "It looks like there are rubies in the water."

"Rubies!" shouted Dan.

"We've found a buried treasure!" called Ted.

Robin laughed, "a 'berried' treasure!"

"Berry funny, Robin!" said Mr. Parks.

Everyone laughed!

Dear Sapna,
We went on a trip to a cranberry marsh. It was interesting. I am sending you some pictures. The brochure said there is a cranberry marsh in Aylesford. You live near there. Have you ever been there? If not, you should go.

Your friend,
Kim

Cranberry Harvest

Cranberries do not grow on trees.

Cranberries grow on vines.

In October the marsh is flooded and the cranberries float.

The picker combs the berries off the vines.

The berry-boats are filled with cranberries and collected.

The berries go to the packing house to be air cleaned, sorted, and bagged.

Canadian cranberries are sold all around the world.

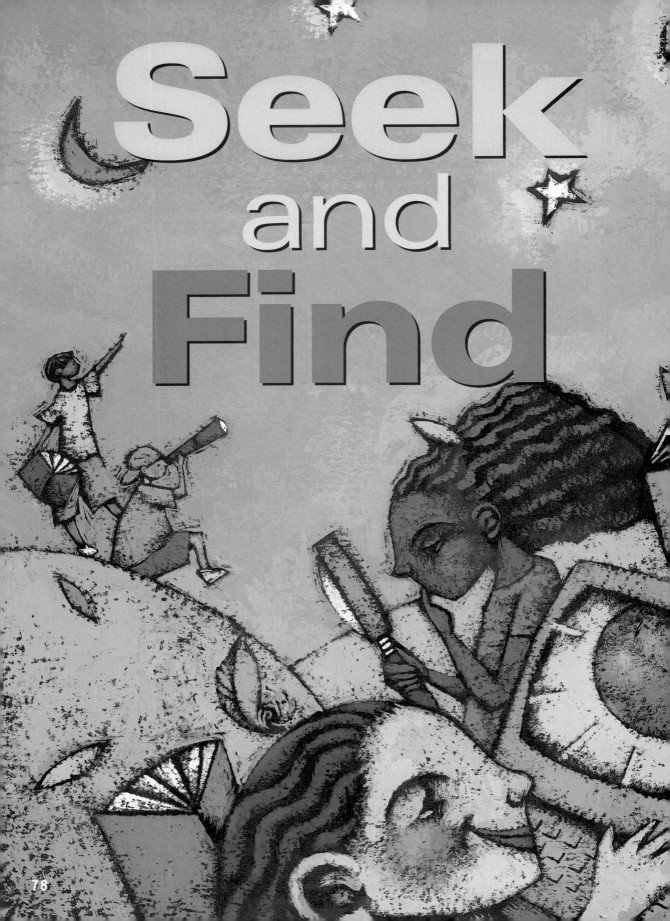

Seek
and
Find

Treasures for Your Mind

Seek and find,
Seek and find,
Searching, collecting
Treasures for your mind.

Your mind is like a treasure chest
Waiting to be filled.
Discover all the good ideas
Upon which you can build.

The more that you find out about,
The richer you will be.
Knowing where to start your search,
That will be the key.

I guess you know the library
Has every kind of book
On many different topics.
Go and take a look.

Magazines and videos,
Encyclopedias too,
Computers and the Internet —
The world is there for you.

Don't forget that people
Have information, too.
Think of questions you could ask
In an interview.

So now go on your treasure hunt,
But not for silver or gold.
Instead, find knowledge. It lasts for years,
Until you're very old.

Seek and find,
Seek and find,
Searching, collecting
Treasures for your mind.

79

Lucy's Picture

Story by Nicola Moon   Pictures by Alex Ayliffe

"My grandpa's coming to visit today," said Lucy.
"How nice," said Mrs. Kelly. "Now, take a seat because we're all going to do some painting."
"Can I do a picture for Grandpa?" asked Lucy.
"Of course you may," said Mrs. Kelly.

Lucy looked at the big sheet of white paper in front of her.

"Can't you think of what to paint, Lucy?" asked Mrs. Kelly.

"What would your grandpa like? Something nice and bright? Look at those lovely colours!"

Lucy looked at the red and the yellow and the sky-blue paints. "They're not right," she said. "May I use the glue? May I stick things on to make a picture?"

"You mean a collage? Of course! But you'll have to sit at another table. There's not enough room here."

Lucy took her paper to an empty table in the corner. She went and found a bottle of glue, some scissors, and the box of scraps.

Lucy loved Mrs. Kelly's box of scraps. She liked plunging her hands deep in the box and feeling with her eyes shut.

Lucy started her picture. She cut some soft green velvet into curvy mounds for hills, and stuck some of them on the paper. She made a lake out of blue shiny stuff, and put it in between the hills.

Then she found some flowery dress material.

"Grandpa has flowers like this in his garden," Lucy told Mrs. Kelly. Lucy cut around the flowers and stuck them in little clumps along the edge of the lake.

At recess Lucy was too busy to play. Instead she collected twigs, leaves, and two small feathers. Then she filled her empty juice cup with sand from the sandbox. At last it was time to go inside.

Now Lucy was even more excited about Grandpa's picture. She made him a tree out of twigs and the leaves, and stuck the feathers on the end of a branch. Then she squeezed a long winding ribbon of glue over the hills, and sprinkled sand over the glue to make a path.

"My grandpa's got a dog," Lucy told Mrs. Kelly. "She's called Honey because that's what colour she is."

When Mrs. Kelly wasn't looking, Lucy trimmed a piece of her own hair and glued it to a dog she had made from a piece of paper.

"That's lovely, Lucy," said Mrs. Kelly when it was storytime. She put Lucy's picture safely on the side to dry along with all the paintings.

Lucy couldn't wait to go home. She hadn't seen Grandpa in a long time.

Her mother was waiting as usual, but today there was someone with her.

"Grandpa," cried Lucy. She nearly knocked him off his feet.

"I made you a picture, Grandpa. Look...." Lucy grabbed her blind grandfather's hand and guided it over the picture. "These are hills, and here's the road...."

Grandpa touched the picture carefully. "A tree, a bird. And what's this? It feels like your hair, Lucy.

"That's Honey!" said Lucy, smiling.

"How clever! And what a wonderful surprise. It's the best picture I've ever seen," said Grandpa. And hand in hand, Grandpa and Lucy and her mother walked home.

Treasure Hunting

"That was a great story, Mr. Parks," said Anna.
"I like the way Lucy looked for special treasures
to put in her picture," said Dan.
" Me too, "said Gus. "I love books."

Mr. Parks smiled," Yes, books tell wonderful stories, but they are also good tools for getting information. Finding information is like going on a treasure hunt — a treasure hunt for your brain. Let's brainstorm to see what comes to mind when you think about places to look for information."

OUR TREASURE HUNTING TOOLS FOR RESEARCH

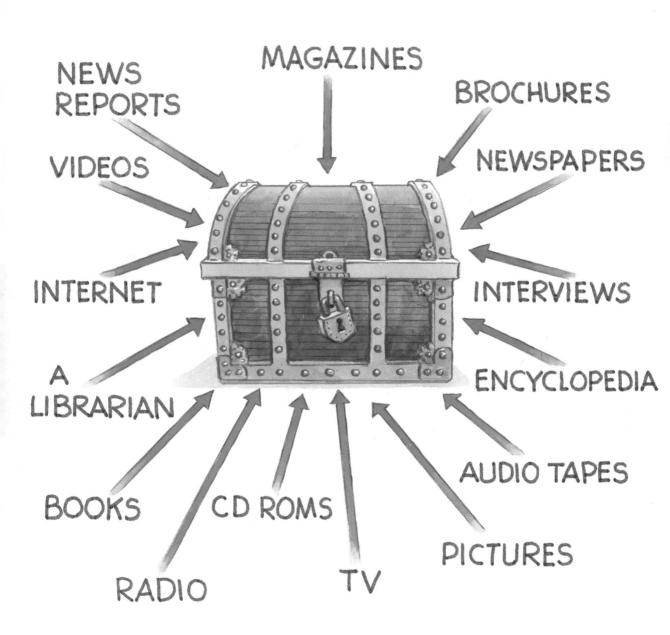

NEWS REPORTS

MAGAZINES

BROCHURES

VIDEOS

NEWSPAPERS

INTERNET

INTERVIEWS

A LIBRARIAN

ENCYCLOPEDIA

AUDIO TAPES

BOOKS

CD ROMS

PICTURES

RADIO

TV

Mr. Parks and the children thought and thought.
Before long they had a chart full of good ideas.

"You have done a wonderful job of brainstorming," said Mr. Parks. "Remember the more tools you use the better the treasure becomes."

Robin said, "I'm going to the library to get all those tools for my raven project."

"Robin," laughed Gus. "Don't take the whole library home with you!"

"If you did that, you'd need a van," said Dan.

"Or a pickup truck!" laughed Ted.

Mr. Parks smiled. "Not the whole library at once, Robin. Use one tool at a time."

The children thought about what they wanted to learn and what tools to use.

"Raj knows about magnets. I'll write to him," said Dan.

"How high can a hot air balloon go?" asked Ted.

"My Mom and I can find information for you on the Internet," said Robin.

"I want to know about the place where my grandmother was born. What should I use, Mr. Parks?" asked Anna.

"An encyclopedia or an atlas," answered Mr. Parks.

"I'll look for a video about learning to draw," said Kim.

"I went to a special celebration on the weekend," said Gus. "Is there a CD-ROM about celebrations?"

Bud said,"There's a zillion things to think about. I''ll ask the librarian to help me."

"My," said Mr. Parks,"you have so many exciting ideas. What a busy year you will have filling your treasure chests. Have fun seeking and finding."

Treasure Box

by Judy Ann Sadler

Now you can make your own treasure chest. Fill it with your special treasures.

You will need
- decorating materials
- a shoebox with a lid
- a container for glue mixture
- scraps of wrapping paper or magazine pictures
- scissors
- a paint brush
- white glue

1 Cut or tear the paper into different-sized pieces.

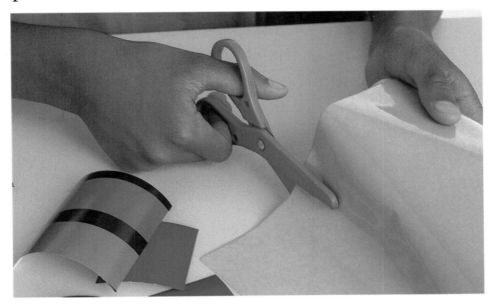

2 Mix equal amounts of white glue and water in a container.

3 Brush an area of the shoebox with the glue mixture. Smooth on pieces of paper. Repeat until the box and the lid are completely covered.

4 Glue on decorations such as glitter, sequins, buttons, beads, ribbon, or lace.

5 Once your shoe box is dry, it is ready to hold your treasures.

Animal Tales

In My Pocket

Did you know there's a wonderful zoo in my pocket?
Leaves and a ship, yes, all in my pocket!
Some folks have pockets to carry their keys,
To carry some tissues for when they might sneeze.
Not me, I have animals, perhaps more than one.
You might too, when all's said and done.

First there's a beaver so shiny and sleek.
Then there's a caribou. Quick, take a peek.
There's a loon who is quietly taking a swim.
And then a huge polar bear — don't forget him!
There are also some leaves; they are maple I think,
And a beautiful ship. I hope it won't sink.

So check in your pocket and look for the zoo.
Oh yes, and you might find a queen in there, too!

Fun With Coins

Coin Hunt

Can you find two coins that do not have animals on them? Draw them.

Rub, Rub, Rub

You can make a coin rubbing. Take a piece of plain paper. Place the coin under the paper (tail side showing). Get a pencil. Rub the pencil over the hidden coin. What do you see?

Rub a few coins on the same page. How much are all the coins you rubbed worth?

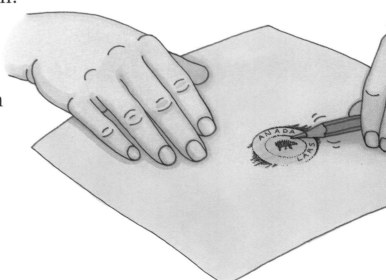

An Amazing Coin Trick

Put a coin on the top of your desk or table. Hold a magnet underneath the table or desk. Make sure that the magnet is directly under your coin. Move the magnet under the table or desk. What do you see? Can you explain what happens?

Caribou Coin

The animal on the back of a quarter is a caribou. Many people mistake it for a moose. Find out how a moose and a caribou are the same and different.

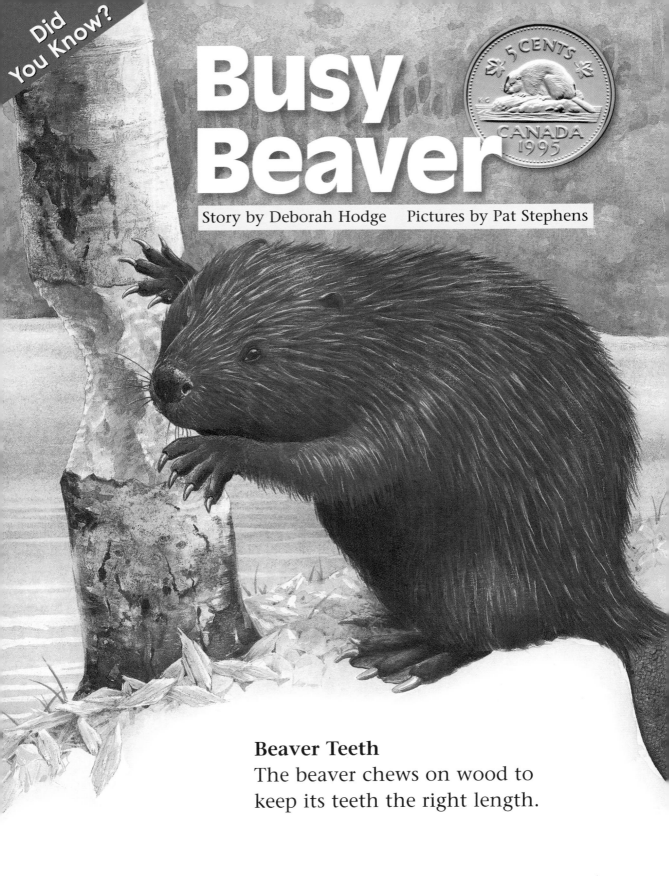

Busy Beaver

Story by Deborah Hodge   Pictures by Pat Stephens

Beaver Teeth
The beaver chews on wood to keep its teeth the right length.

Where Beavers Live

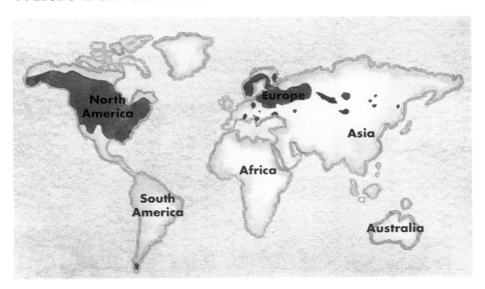

Beaver Food

Beavers are plant eaters. They feed on tree bark all year round. In spring and summer, they also eat new green plants.

Every fall, beavers in northern areas store food for winter. They cut trees into small pieces and then stack the wood near their lodge. All winter long, they eat from this food pile.

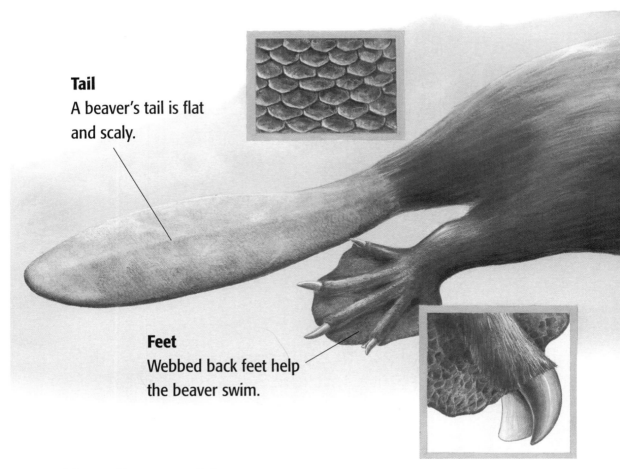

Tail
A beaver's tail is flat and scaly.

Feet
Webbed back feet help the beaver swim.

How Beavers Move
A beaver's body is long and smooth in the water. This helps it to glide. Beavers often stay underwater for two or three minutes at a time.

A Beaver Dam
When beavers move into an area, they usually build a dam. The dam is like a wall across a stream. Water trapped behind it forms a deep pond. The beavers are safer in the deep water. Here they can build a home, store food, and escape enemies.

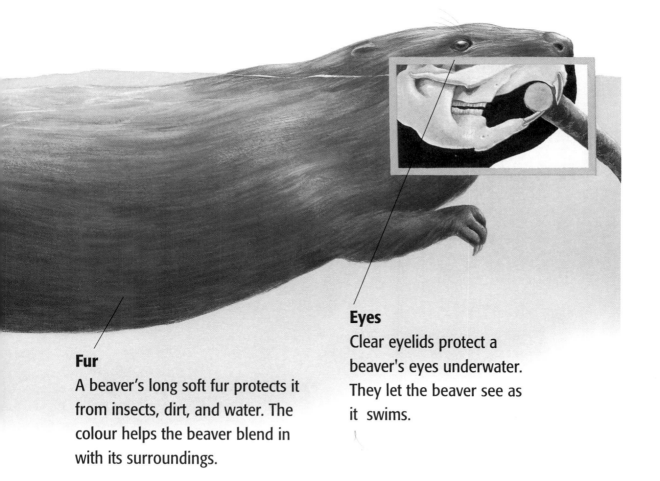

Fur

A beaver's long soft fur protects it from insects, dirt, and water. The colour helps the beaver blend in with its surroundings.

Eyes

Clear eyelids protect a beaver's eyes underwater. They let the beaver see as it swims.

A Beaver Lodge

A beaver home is called a lodge. Beavers build their lodge in the deep pond behind their dam. Like the dam, the lodge is made by piling up sticks, rocks, and mud. It takes a pair of beavers about a week to build a lodge. They add to it and repair it often.

Beaver Babies

Beaver babies are called kits. The newborn kits are covered with thick fur. Their eyes are open and their teeth are sharp. As soon as they are born, the kits can see, hear, walk, and swim.

Who Will Be the Ruler?

Adapted from an African folk tale • Pictures by Barbara Spurll

The old moose had been king of the forest for a long time. He had watched over the emerald green trees, the tall pines, the silver birches, and the forest flowers. He had been the great protector of all the animals, birds, and insects.

All the creatures bowed with respect whenever his majesty passed by. The animals were always happy to see his majestic antlers. They were like a shield of safety.

One day, he called all the animals to a meeting near the marsh. He raised his throne stick high.

"It is time for you to have a new ruler. I am getting old and want to rest now. Whoever can throw this silver birch stick high into the sky and count to ten before it hits the ground will be the new ruler," said the moose. Everyone thought, "That will be easy."

"I will go first," said the deer. "I am swift and fast." The deer threw the silver stick up into the air and counted, "One, two, three, four, five, six...." — The stick hit the ground.

Up stepped the bobcat. "I am strong and I can climb high," boasted the bobcat. The bobcat flung the silver stick up in the air and counted, "One, two, three, four, five, six, seven…." The stick hit the ground.

The wolf stepped forward. He said, "I am fast and I am the leader of my pack." He hurled the silver stick high into the air and counted, "One, two, three, four, five, six, seven, eight...." The stick hit the ground.

A bear stood up on her hind legs. She bragged, "I am big and I am strong. I can throw the silver stick and win. Watch me!" All the animals stared. She *was* big and strong. There was not a sound in the forest.

The bear took a deep breath and sent the stick flying high into the sky. She counted, "One, two, three, four, five, six, seven, eight, nine…." The stick hit the ground.

"Who would be next?" they all thought. If the bear could not do it, no one could. No one came forward.

His majesty, the moose, bellowed, "Is there anyone else?"

A quiet voice said, "I would like to try." Everyone turned to look. It was the beaver.

"You? You think you can do this?" they all asked.

His majesty nodded and said, "Give it your best shot!"

The beaver picked up the silver stick and threw it high into the sky. She counted, "Two, four, six, eight, ten." She caught the stick before it touched the ground.

"Oh, how wise you are," said the moose, "— wise enough to be our queen." All the animals cheered.

Loon

Splendid feathers,
Black and white,
Pearly collar,
Eyes so bright.

Haunting call,
Through the night,
Distant, long,
'Til morning light.

Bird of the North,
Reach out to me.
Touch me with
Your serenity.

DOZAY CHRISTMAS

How is this picture like a dream?
How does it make you feel?

Artist's Corner

What can you learn about the loon by looking at this picture?

What story does this picture tell?

Can you see a bird in this artist's work? Is it a loon? Could it be another bird?

This work does not have a title. What would you call it? Why?

Raven

Coal black eyes,
Cunning,
Wise,
Watching,
Waking,
Imitating,
Raven tell your tale to me.

Bird of mystery,
Bird of history,
Feathers gleaming,
Ever dreaming,
Raven tell your tale to me.

Soaring high
Through the sky,
Black wings spreading,
Are you heading
Down to tell your tale to me?

A Special Coin

Fact 1
This $200 Canadian coin is called "Raven Bringing Light to the World."

Fact 2
Robert Davidson first made the design for a small pendant.

Fact 3
The design is about a very old Haida story.

Fact 4
The coin is made mostly of fine gold. It has some fine silver in it too.

Fact 5
The coin's diameter is 29 millimetres.

RAVEN
Bringing Light to the World

Raven is an important character in many Haida stories. He loves to play tricks but he can also be a hero.

When Haida artist Robert Davidson made this work of art, he was thinking of a very old Haida story about Raven, called "How Raven Brought Light to the World." In this story, there is darkness everywhere on earth. The Chief owns the sun but he will not share its light. Only *he* may open the box that holds the light.

Raven wants to give the light to the people of the world. He makes a plan to trick the Chief. First he pretends that he is the Chief's grandson. Then he tricks the Chief into promising

anything he wants. Raven asks to see the light, but the Chief does not want to show it to him. For many days, Raven asks the Chief again and again to show him the light. Finally, the Chief opens the box. Quickly, Raven snatches the light and flies out of the smoke hole into the dark sky.

Some of the light becomes the sun. Some of it becomes the stars. And some of it becomes the moon. To this day, whenever people marvel at the lights in the sky, they remember the gift Raven gave the earth.

Where can you look for other stories about Raven? When you find one, share it with others in your class.

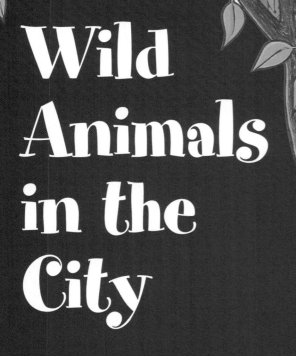

Wild Animals in the City

When the sun sets and the
day is done, the animals
come out, one by one.

On the ground and in the
tree — can you see them?
Look carefully!

There are No Polar Bears Here!

Story by Catherine Simpson   Pictures by Joanne Snook

One Saturday in May, Kerry was picking
partridgeberries on the hill above the Cove.
   She was bending over, getting her fingers red
with squashy berries when she heard a snuffle and
a whuffle. She looked up. There, on the slope
above her, stood a bear. A polar bear. Jumpins!

Kerry had learned about bears in school. She didn't panic. She pushed her bucket of berries towards the bear and backed away slowly.
The bear shuffled forward and started to munch.

Kerry ran back to the Cove. The first person she saw was Uncle Ron, fixing his fence.

"I saw a polar bear!" she said.

"Impossible, my duckie. There are no polar bears here," he said.

"Yes there are," said Kerry. "I saw one. I know a bear when I see one."

Kerry ran on until she spotted Aunt Jean, hanging clothes.

"I saw a polar bear!" she said.

"Impossible, my trout. There are no polar bears here," she answered.

"Yes, there are," said Kerry. "I saw one. I know a bear when I see one."

Nobody would believe her.

Next morning, Kerry took a shortcut to school through a patch of woods where hummocks of leftover snow still lay hard and white in the shady places. Ahead of her on the path, a particularly large hummock was hulking. It was no snowdrift. Jumpins!

She didn't panic. She spoke softly and unwrapped her lunch. "Hello again, bear. Have my partridgeberry bun." She tossed it out into the woods and the bear shuffled after it, snuffling and whuffling.

At school, Kerry told her news.

"Are you sure it wasn't a sheep?" asked Thomas.

"Are you sure it wasn't a sheepdog?" asked Isabel.

"Are you sure it wasn't an iceberg?" asked Tracey.

"It must have been a figment of your imagination," said Ms. Primmer.

Kerry rolled her eyes and sighed. "It was a bear. I know a bear when I see one."

Nobody would believe her.

So after school, Kerry went to see someone she knew would believe her — her grandmother.

"I saw a polar bear," she said.

"Where?" asked her grandmother.

"Up above the Cove, on our back steps, and on the shortcut. But nobody will believe me."

"Why not?" asked her grandmother.

"They think I'm making it up. They say there are no polar bears here."

"Maybe they need to see it with their own eyes," her grandmother said.

She gave Kerry a tin of partridgeberry squares. "See you at the bean supper tonight."

Kerry had forgotten about the bean supper. Everyone in the Cove would be there. If only the bear could be there too! But how could she get him to go there?

If she were a detective, she could track him down and turn him in.

If she were a cowboy, she could go out and round him up.

If she were a fisherman, she could scoop him up in a net.

If she were a starship commander, she could beam him up in a shower of glitter.

Kerry sighed. It was useless. There was no way to get the bear to the bean supper, unless ... Bingo! She had an idea.

She rummaged in her schoolbag, took out a pencil and paper, and printed in large letters:

> *Dear Bear:*
> *Please come to the bean supper tonight so that everyone will see you.*
> *Your friend,*
> *Kerry*

Then she placed the invitation beside Puzzle Rock and anchored it with a partridgeberry square.

That evening everyone in the Cove went to the bean supper in the community hall. Kerry's whole family went, along with her grandfather and grandmother. Uncle Ron and Aunt Jean and all the kids from school went, too, with their brothers and sisters and fathers and mothers and grandfathers and grandmothers and cousins and even their second cousins once removed.

Everyone sat down and feasted on beans baked in molasses. For dessert, there was partridgeberry pudding. But Kerry couldn't touch a bite. Her stomach was full of butterflies. Would he or wouldn't he show up?

The hall got hotter and hotter.

Someone groaned, "My, how hot it is! Open the door before we all cook!"

Uncle Ron braced the door open. A cool breeze drifted in. Suddenly, Kerry sat bolt upright. What was that sound?

It was a snuffle.

Then she heard another sound, closer.

It was a whuffle.

Then came a shuffle, shuffle, shuffle.

And right through the open door came a wiggly black nose, followed by a big white polar bear body. Jumpins!

Kerry wanted to run and kiss him, but she knew he wouldn't appreciate that, so she took her pudding and put it on the floor in front of him. He munched gratefully.

First there was silence from the crowd behind her. Then there was a huge gasp — AHHHHHRRRGG!

"Jumpins! Help! A polar bear! We thought she was makin' it all up! Call the cops! Call the wildlife! Call the fire department!"

Kerry stood smiling at the panic. Now, at last, everyone believed her. She turned to thank the bear, but — he was gone. Vanished. Just like that!

She ran outside. She saw houses, lines of wash, hummocks of old snow, sheep on the hills, ice in the harbour. But where was the bear?

"There you are!" she whispered.

There he was, just a speck far out on the salt water, swimming back to the ice edge, back to the North. At least, she thought it was the bear. It might have been a piece of ice.

But probably not. After all, Kerry knows a bear when she sees one.

Beary Funny

JOKE 1:
What pie do polar bears eat?

Answer: (Blue**beary** pie)

JOKE 2:
Where does the polar bear like to cook a fish?

Answer: (On the **bear** b que.)

JOKE 3:
Why don't polar bears look at their reflection in the water?

Answer: (They think they look un**bear**able.)

JOKE 4:

Why don't polar bears like to walk through the snow?

Answer: (They have **bear** feet.)

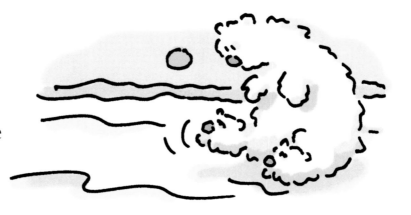

JOKE 5:

Where does the polar bear get a hair cut?

Answer: (At the bar**bear**!)

JOKE 6:

What do polar bears think about these jokes?

Answer: (They can't **bear** them.)

Tails

Long tails, short tails,
Bushy tails too.
Curly tails, cotton tails,
Tails old and new.

Tails used for swinging
And wagging to and fro.
Tails used for warning,
And protection long ago.

Tails used for balance,
To flip, flop, splash.
Tails used for swatting,
As quick as a flash.

Tails used to show off
Their beauty to a mate.
Tails used for rudders
To keep things straight.

Tails would look funny
On a mouth or a nose.
That's why they're attached
At the end, I suppose.

Animal Riddles

Make up a riddle about
a loon,
a caribou,
a beaver,
or another animal.

Share your riddle with a partner.

Write a silly story about how the pig got a curly tail or the beaver got a flat tail.

Write three facts that you learned in Animal Tales that you would like to remember. What can you do to help you remember them?

Animal Guessing Game

Look in magazines. Find pictures of different animals. Cut out some ears, feet, noses, or eyes. Paste them on a sheet of paper. Number them. Can your partner guess what animal each one belongs to? (Keep a list of the right answers.)